Disney · PIXAR

Cars

Party Time!

Parragon

First published by Parragon in 2011

Parragon
Queen Street House
4 Queen Street
Bath BA1 1HE, UK

ISBN 978-1-4454-1828-5
Printed in China.

Contents

Party checklist

Organization is key to planning a party.
Use the checklist below to keep on track.

> Check with your parents.

> Pick a date.

> Pick an awesome venue.

> Choose your start and finish times.

> Write a guest list.

> Make your invitations.

> Hand out or send the invitations.

> Decide how you're going to
make the venue look cool.

> Write a list of food and drinks.

> Arrange some games.

> Organize the music.

Checklist tips

Getting your parents to agree to a party is probably the most important step. Offering to help out should increase the chances of them saying . . .

"YES!"

When you're deciding who to invite, think about friends, neighbors, and relatives. Everyone will make new friends, as well as hang out with their old ones.

TOP TIP!

Use this book to help you with everything listed here.

Make: Party Invitations

You'll need some plain paper or construction paper, pens, ruler, scissors, a coffee mug, and a paper clip.

1

Draw twice round the mug on to some card to make two circles. Cut them out. Fold one circle in half and then half again.

2

Open it up. The fold lines will mark the quarters and middle of the circle. Cut a v-shape out of one quarter—not quite reaching the center of the circle.

cut
out

3

Put the two circles together (put the one with the cut-out v-shape on the top). Push the paper clip through the middle and open it out at the back.

4

Turn the top circle round and write your invitation details in each quarter. Decorate the top with pictures of your favorite Cars.

Once you've made your invitations, make sure you include all the information about the party.

❯ **The occasion (e.g. a Lightning party!)**

❯ **Your name.**

❯ **The name of the person you're inviting.**

❯ **The date.**

❯ **The time the party starts and finishes.**

❯ **The venue (including the address).**

❯ **The theme, so the guest knows what to bring and wear.**

❯ **"RSVP" (this tells the guest you'd like a reply to the invitation).**

❯ **Your phone number.**

Guest List

Guest:. . . . .

Where to deliver invitation: . . . .

. . . .

Guest:. . . . .

Where to deliver invitation: . . . .

. . . .

Guest:. . . . .

Where to deliver invitation: . . . .

. . . .

Guest:. . . . .

Where to deliver invitation: . . . .

. . . .

Guest:. . . . .

Where to deliver invitation: . . . .

. . . .

Guest:. . . . .

Where to deliver invitation: . . . .

Guest:. . . . .

Where to deliver invitation: . . . .

. . . .

Guest:. . . . .

Where to deliver invitation: . . . .

. . . .

Guest:. . . . .

Where to deliver invitation: . . . .

. . . .

Guest:. . . . .

Where to deliver invitation: . . . .

. . . .

Guest:. . . . .

Where to deliver invitation: . . . .

. . . .

Guest:. . . . .

Where to deliver invitation: . . .

. . . .

. . . .

. . . .

9

Party Themes

Deciding on a theme for your party is the most important step. Look at the themes on these pages, and pick the one that sounds the coolest! Once you've decided, sorting the food, decorations, and everything else will be easy.

Team Lightning McQueen

Lightning's pit stop crew are the fastest on the circuit. Ask your friends to wear a pit crew outfit. They should choose a color (e.g. blue for Doc), and make headsets from old headphones.

First to the Finish

This party theme is all about being a racing champion. Hang checkered flags in your venue, and use the game pages of this book to organize awesome racing games!

Desert Driving

The desert throws up some harsh terrain. Sarge is the expert on dodging rocks. Try to make your venue look like the desert track. Make race markers out of cardboard!

Fast Lane Fame

Are you a slidin', glidin' star like Lightning? If the answer's yes, you should choose this theme. Let your friends know that you're the champion, but make everyone feel like a star!

Arriving At The Race

From the minute your guests walk up to your party, they'll know it's the speediest, sparkiest party ever. Here are some things you can do to get everyone's engines running. Vroom vroom!

License to Drive

Set up a table at your front door where all new drivers have to sign up for their license to drive!

Use card to create mini drivers' licenses with your guests' names and photos.

Decorate the license with stickers and add a hole and some string, so you can hang it around their neck.

Car-parazzi

Paint a large picture of your favorite car on a piece of cardboard.

Add two smaller pieces of cardboard on the back to make it stand up.

Set this up before your guests arrive, and they can have their fan picture snapped on the way in!

Start Your Engines

Lightning McQueen would want to get straight into the action, so don't keep your guests hanging about. Try some of these quick pit-stop games to get the party started . . .

Which Car am I?

1. Prepare small cards with pictures and names of the *Cars* characters.

2. Get all your guests into a circle and tape a card to each of their backs.

3. The players walk around and their friends can give them one clue about which Car they are, like "your number is 95" for Lightning, "you're sponsored by Dinoco" for The King, and "you're Lightning's best friend" for Mater.

4. When you've guessed your character you can try to help your friends!

100+

Welcome to
Radiator Springs!

1. Make a sign for each corner of the room to represent a different spot in Radiator Springs— The Cozy Cone Motel, Luigi's Casa Della Tires, Sarge's Surplus Hut, and Flo's V8 Café.

2. Start playing car-themed music in the background and when the music stops, all the players have to run to 'visit' one of the locations.

3. But watch out! One location will be shouted out, and if you're in that corner, you're out of the game!

4. Keep going until there's one person left—the winner!

Party Pit Stop

Even Lightning McQueen has got to stop for gas.
Remember to ask a grown up to help when using sharp knives,
operating the stove or oven, and utilizing kitchen appliances.

Flo's V8 Cafe

Flo can fill up your party guests with sweet treats
to keep them running all day! Set up your café
by covering your snack table with black paper, to
represent the road. Pin up a 'Flo's V8 Café' sign so
your guests know where to pull in for their fuel! Use
black-and-white paper plates and napkins to keep
the checker-flag color theme. Sweet!

Car-themed treats!

You can use the party shapes from this book to make cool *Cars* sandwiches, and find the recipe for racing star cookies on page 20. If you want to try some character-themed food, why not go for 'Mack' and cheese, or 'Tow Mater' pasta.

Fillmore's Organic Fuel

Now it's time for some fuel, and Fillmore's got just the stuff! Use the recipe on page 18 to make some awesome smoothies.

Create a Fillmore sign for the drinks station. Get creative and name your drinks to look like car fuels, and use the punch-out flags from this book to make cool drinks' markers!

Food: Fruity Fuel

Make cool smoothies to refuel your party guests!

You will need

For a strawberry and mango smoothie:

4 strawberries
¾ cup sliced mango
1 small banana
Juice of 1 orange
3 tablespoons low fat yogurt
1 tablespoon honey
Blender container
Glass and straws

Why not make a cool fruit lolly using your smoothie? Just pour the mixture into a tray, add a lolly stick, and put it in the freezer.

Chop three strawberries, the mango, and the banana. Put them in the bowl with all the other ingredients.

1

Blend everything until you have a smooth, thick mixture.

2

Pour the smoothie into a glass. Add straws that are the color of your favorite racing car!

3

19

Food: Racing Stars

These awesome treats will keep your party revving.
Vroom vroom!

- Large mixing bowl
- Sieve
- 2¼ cups all-purpose flour
- Pinch of salt
- I teaspoon baking powder
- 1 tablespoon butter
- ¾ cup light brown sugar
- 2 eggs, beaten
- 2 ounces corn syrup
- 3 ounces semi-sweet chocolate
- Rolling pin, a cookie cutter
- Nonstick cooking spray
- Baking sheet

1 Pre-heat the oven to 325°F. Sift the flour, salt, and baking powder into a large bowl.

2 With your fingers, rub the butter into the dry ingredients. Add the sugar. In a cup, stir together the eggs and the corn syrup.

With a wooden spoon, beat the ingredients until they are thoroughly combined. Break the chocolate into small chunks and add to the mixture.

3

Place the dough on a board. Sprinkle it lightly with flour so it doesn't stick to the rolling pin. Roll out the dough until it's about half an inch thick. Using your racing star press-out piece, cut out star-shaped cookies.

4

Lightly grease a baking sheet with non-stick cooking spray. Place the cookies about 2 inches apart on the baking sheet. Bake for 15mins until golden.

5

Food: Cheesy Sticks

What you need:
- ❯ **1 cup plain flour, plus extra for dusting**
- ❯ **½ tsp paprika (optional)**
- ❯ **Half a stick of margarine, plus extra for greasing**
- ❯ **1/2 cup grated Parmesan cheese**
  - ❯ **1 egg, lightly beaten**

makes: **16**
prep: **10 minutes**
cooking: **10 minutes**
oven temp: **400°F**

Equipment
- ❯ **2 baking trays**
- ❯ **Sieve**
- ❯ **Mixing bowl**
- ❯ **Fork**
- ❯ **Rolling pin**
- ❯ **Wire cooling rack**

1

Heat the oven to 400°F. Lightly grease two baking trays with margarine.

Sift the flour and the paprika, if using, into a mixing bowl. Break the margarine into pieces, then add to the bowl.

2

100+

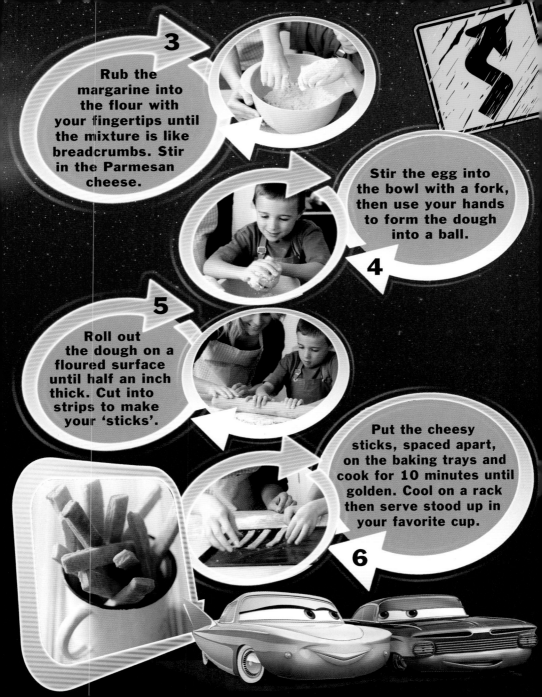

3 Rub the margarine into the flour with your fingertips until the mixture is like breadcrumbs. Stir in the Parmesan cheese.

Stir the egg into the bowl with a fork, then use your hands to form the dough into a ball. **4**

5 Roll out the dough on a floured surface until half an inch thick. Cut into strips to make your 'sticks'.

Put the cheesy sticks, spaced apart, on the baking trays and cook for 10 minutes until golden. Cool on a rack then serve stood up in your favorite cup. **6**

Speedway Games

Are you ready? Now it's time for some awesome games—so cool that you'll feel as if you're hangin' out with the whole Cars crew!

Mack, Mack, Lightning!

To play this game you gotta be quicker than quick!

1. Players sit in a circle, facing inward, and someone is chosen to start as Doc Hudson. Doc is the 'picker' and should walk around the outside of the circle, looking for a partner for a super-speedy race!

2. As he passes he taps each player on the head, calling them 'Mack' out loud, until he finally taps someone and calls them 'Lightning'. Lightning then jumps up and chases Doc!

3. If Doc can make it all the way around the circle and back to sit down in Lightning's spot, then Lightning is the new picker. But if Lightning can tag Doc before he gets there then Lightning can go back to his seat and Doc plays again.

Tractor Tipping

When Mater takes Lightning out tractor tipping, he thinks it's the funniest thing EVER! Now you can join in!

1. Ask all the players to walk around the room to music, pretending to drive.

2. When the music stops, a horn will sound, just like the kind of sound Mater makes to scare the tractors!

3. As soon as the players hear the horn, they have to sit down on the ground, but they better be fast—the last one to the floor is out!

Game: Headlight Hunt

When Lightning loses Mack he realizes how important headlights can be! Now it's your turn to search in the dark.

1. Close a room off and shut all the blinds and curtains to make it as dark as possible.

2. Hide a number of *Cars* characters in the room—if you don't have the toys, then print out colored images of them.

3. Now put your guests in teams of two, and give them a torch and a clue about a Car. They have to work out the clue and find the matching Car in the room!

4. The quickest team to find their Car with their 'headlight' wins.

Game: Turbo Tyre Change

**Lightning's had a blow-out,
and he needs your help!**

1. Put a big picture of Lightning McQueen on the wall, and blank out one of his tires.

2. Glue the picture of that tire onto cardboard, and put some adhesive putty on the back.

3. Now players take turns to be blindfolded and try to 'change' Lightning's tire by pinning it back in the right spot.
Good luck crew!

Checkered Flag Quiz

Are you the biggest *Cars* fan ever? Let's find out!
Put your guests into two teams and let each team decide
on a buzzer noise—one team can say 'Ka-chow' and the
other can say 'Beep-beep'. Now ask the questions
and see who can get the most points.

1. **What number is Lightning McQueen?**
   A. 95
   B. 43
   C. 86

2. **What's the name of Lightning's sponsor company?**
   A. Dinoco
   B. Rust-eze
   C. Wimpy's

3. **Who runs the Cozy Cone Motel?**
   A. Sally
   B. Doc
   C. Luigi

4. **What's the name of the newspaper that Doc shows Lightning?**
   A. The Racing Times
   B. The Piston Paper
   C. The Daily Exhaust

5. What is Mater the best at in the world?

A. Chasing tractors

B. Driving backwards

C. Repairing roads

6. Where is Radiator Springs?

A. In Raceway Region

B. In Speedway Central

C. In Carburetor County

7. What nickname does Sally give Lightning?

A. Hotrod

B. Stickers

C. Thunderbolt

8. How does Mack lose Lightning?

A. He falls asleep

B. He slips on the road

C. He gets bashed by another truck

9. What is Doc's old racing name?

A. Strip Weathers

B. Fabulous Hudson Hornet

C. Doctor Checker

10. What has Mater always wanted to do?

A. Race in the LA International Speedway

B. Ride in Mack's trailer

C. Fly in a helicopter

Ramone's House of Body Art

Ramone loves giving his friends brand-new paint jobs. Create a 'coloring corner' in your house filled with construction paper and paints, and get creative!

Face Painting

Now everyone has the chance to look like their favorite car! Get painted with colors, designs, or numbers to match the characters in the movie.

Car-toon Station

Give everyone a big sheet of paper and some colored markers. Everyone gets a chance to design their own brand new car—what it looks like, what it's called, and what it can do!

Doc's Door Signs

Everyone can decorate
their room like Doc's Clinic!
He has totally cool signs on
his door saying 'Private
Property' and 'Keep Out'.
Give your party-goers
pieces of rectangle card to
create signs for their own
bedroom doors.

Licensed to Thrill

Give your party goers the license
plate templates from the back
of this book, and some poster
paints and stickers. Then get busy
creating your own cars license
plates. Don't forget to come up
with a cool registration like 'AWE
SOME'. Ramone's plate reads
'LOWNSLO', meaning 'low and slow'.

Make: Party Favor Box

At the back of this book, you'll find press-out templates for a *Cars* gift box. You can either make one box from the template, or copy the shape on to construction paper and make your own! The boxes are perfect for handing out party favors to your guests.

Box Base

1: Press out the 'Box Base Template'

2: Fold the four sides upward, using the creases as a guide.

3: Fold down the flaps on the top and bottom, and fold in the tabs.

4: Fold down the flaps on the right and left sides, over the tabs.

5: Press the creases into place, so that your Box Base stays together.

Box Top

Follow steps 2 to 5 to put your Box Top together.

Place your Box Top over your Box Base to create your beautiful gift box.

Make: Food Flags

At the back of this book you'll find punch-out templates for handy food flags. You can copy the the shape on to construction paper and make more of your own! The flags are perfect for labeling your party food.

You'll need: cocktail sticks

1: Press out the flag shapes.

2: Fold along the creases.

3: Place a cocktail stick where the flag is folded, and add a piece of sticky tape to hold in place.

4: Write the name of the food on the flag, so everyone knows what's what!

Make: Photo Frames

At the back of this book, you'll find two awesome punch-out photo frames. They are perfect for holding cool photos of your party.

1: Press out the photo frame (front and back pieces).

2: Cut your photograph to the same size as the photo frame back.

3: Use some glue to stick the photograph to the photo frame back.

4: Glue the photo frame front on top of your photo, to create a super-cool frame.

5: Place your photo frame on the wall where all your fans can see it!

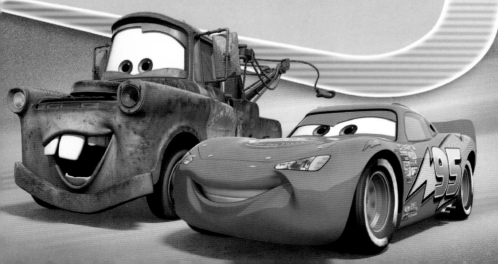

Make: Tool Box

At the back of this book, you'll find punch-out pieces to make this super-cool tool box. Put candy inside to make party favors for your friends!

1: Press out the Tool Box template.

2: Fold up all four sides along the creases.

3: Insert the tabs into the slits in the template.

100

Make: Party Box

Punch out the Party Box pieces at the back of this book to make more super-cool party favor boxes.

1: Fold up all four sides along the creases.

2: Insert the tabs into the slits in the template.

3: Fold down the top, and twist the tabs to close.

Racing Games

Rev your engines for the most exciting races since
Lightning McQueen took on Chick Hicks and The King!

**These games are best played
outside with a lot of space.**

Chick's Tire Blow-out

If you don't watch, then ka-blam!

1. Tie a balloon on to each player's ankle with string.
   This will be their 'tire'.

2. The aim of the game is to run around and burst
   everyone else's 'tire' while making sure you keep
   your own one safe!

4. The last player with their balloon in one piece has
   beaten Chick and is the champion.

Mater Tow Race

Uh-oh, Lightning has run out of gas again!

1. Players should be split into teams and each team is given a hula hoop.

2. Two players get into the hula hoop at a time—'Mater' in the front and 'Lightning' in the back. They have to run around a circle track, and back to their team.

3. The player in the front then moves back and a new player takes the position of Mater. The team keeps going until everyone has had a turn as both Mater and Lightning, then everyone sits down.

4. The first team to finish wins the Tow Race!

Game: Luigi's Tyre Stack

To win this game, you'll have to work as a team! Luigi needs his tires stacked neatly in the yard, but who can make the biggest pile?

1. Divide your players into two teams and give them a pile of inflated inner tubes, to look like car tires.

2. Each player takes a turn to add another ring on to a pile, and the challenge is to stack as many as possible without the pile falling over.

3. The team with the highest pile after three minutes wins!

Game: Guido's Pit Race

Can your team change a tire as quick as Guido can?

1. Divide the party goers into teams and blow up an inner tube for each team.

2. Set out start and finish lines, and prepare an obstacle course for the players, using cones and blocks to create a winding path.

3. Each player takes a turn to roll the tire through the obstacle course and back, ready for the next crew member.

4. The quickest crew to get through the course are pit stop champions! Fantastico!

Movie Game

You can play a game while watching the *Cars* movie.
Give your guests fun actions like these to do as it plays . . .

1. **Stamp your feet when you hear the word 'tire'.**

2. **Shout 'Later Mater' whenever someone says Mater's name.**

3. **Lie down on the floor when 'low and slow' Ramone appears on screen.**

4. **Take a sip of juice every time Fillmore talks.**

My Own Cars Game

Personalize your party by making up your very own game. Write the rules on this page, and get your friends involved in some original party gaming!

The name of my game is: ....

This is how it's played: ....

....

....

....

....

The important rules to remember are:

....

....

....

Slidin' Glidin' Gifts!

You'll need to remember the awesome gifts you were given for your birthday, and who gave you what. That way, you can thank them later on.

Gift: ....

From: ....

Gift: ....

From: ....

Gift: ....

From: ....

Gift: ....

From: ....

Gift: ....

From: ....

Gift: ....

From: ....

Gift: ....

From: ....

Party Favors

At the end of your *coolest party ever*, hand out some of the coolest party favors ever.

1. Use the punch-out pieces at the back of this book to make awesome party favor boxes. You can draw around the pieces onto some construction paper, and make enough boxes for everyone!

2. Before your party, ask your parents to help you buy some cool candy. Find candy with red wrappers to match Lightning's body paint.

3. Find mini toys or puzzles that your friends can enjoy once they get home.

4. Place the candy and notes inside your party favor boxes. These can go inside a bigger party favor bag, along with the awesome toys.

100+

The Finish Line

Awards Ceremony

When you're getting to the end of the party, there's only one thing left to do—award the Piston Cup! Gather all your racers together and pass out mini trophies to everybody, or you could make medals out of gold chocolate coins.

Sarge's Surplus Hut

There may be time for one last pit stop! Have a station set up as Sarge's Surplus Hut with your party favor bags for everyone to take home.

The Daily Exhaust

Instead of regular thank-you notes, you could create your own newspaper front page. Check out the one Doc shows Lightning in the movie for inspiration.

Party Awards

Use this page to remember the coolest party ever!
That way, you'll never forget the rip-roaring time
you had with your racing friends.

The coolest game we played was:

....

The best gift I received was:

....

The best song we listened to was:

....

The best food we ate was:

....

My favorite party memory is:

....